CRANKY COREY

Question Guide

Tanya Popovski

Published by PoP-O Books 2018

www.popobooks.com.au

A catalogue record for this book is available from the National Library of Australia.

Book cover design and formatting services by BookCoverCafe.com

Second edition 2019

ISBN 978-0-6482019-5-3 (pbk)

Contents

Getting Started

Kindergarten and year-1 reading expectations are quite different to those of mid to upper primary. In the early years, the focus is on decoding (learning how to read using symbols, sounds, sentences, and visual features). As the reader moves through the grades, the focus of reading in the classroom is about making meaning. The reader is then taught skills to deepen their understanding in order to read to learn.

The chosen book should be at a level below the reader's reading level. If you judge that the text is too difficult for the reader, choose a book at a lower level. This will allow the reader to concentrate on the meaning of the story, thereby encouraging higher-order thinking.

There is no need for pre-reading since a competent reader at this level will be able to read the text. The book should not be read in one sitting. Ask the comprehension questions after the reader has finished the text on each page. Continue to do this for approximately fifteen to twenty minutes. It is acceptable to take more than two sessions to complete questioning of the story. Go at the pace of the reader.

Tips for Using the Question Guide

The symbol ⭐ indicates that an explanation for the word or phrase used can be found in the list at the back of this guide, which you can refer to for further clarification.

This book should not be seen as a text but rather a conversation of learning. When you have asked the reader each comprehension question, give them time to think before responding. The answers have been provided so you can give the reader the answer, which becomes a teachable moment.⭐

If the reader has limited experience with a particular concept, take the opportunity to explore it further through the use of other resources (books, internet, etc). To use Stop Annoying Me as an example, if the reader has no understanding of the way a bull behaves, the words 'raging bull' will have no meaning. In this instance, you could take a moment to explain.

The answers provided in the **Question Guide** are general, and are given as examples only of acceptable answers. If the reader's answer is not relevant to the text, or cannot be justified with evidence from the text, this becomes a teachable moment. Give the answer, and show how you worked it out. The reader's responses do not have to cover all of the suggested answers.

If the reader's prediction of the title is not relevant to the clues on the page, avoid correcting their prediction straightaway. Instead, wait until they have finished reading the story to address the initial prediction. For example, you could say: 'At the beginning of the story, you predicted that the title would be [*repeat the reader's initial prediction*]. Now that you've read the story, how accurate do you think your prediction was? What clues could you have used on the title page to help you predict more accurately?'

The superscript numbers at the end of the questions relate to the tracking sheets (purchased separately at www.popobooks.com.au) and are linked to the Australian Curriculum.

Comprehension Strategies

Good learners draw on a range of comprehension strategies to deepen their understanding of written text. The *Question Guide* has been intentionally formulated to use the six comprehension strategies to explicitly teach how we understand texts. They are colour coded, with each colour corresponding to one of the six strategies.

Making connections   Learners make connections with self, text and what is happening in the world.

Predicting   Good readers use the information from illustrations, text and experiences to predict what will be read.

Questioning   Good readers clarify meaning and aim for a deeper level of understanding by posing and answering questions.

Monitoring   Good readers know what to do if something in the text doesn't make sense.

Visualising   Good readers bring text to life by creating mental pictures from what they are reading.

Summarising Good readers are able to locate the most important ideas in a text and retell them in their own words.

CRANKY COREY
TANYA POPOVSKI

Title page

Allow the reader to read the title and look at the illustration.

Looking at the front cover, what do you think this narrative is about?[3]
The reader should respond based on the information on the front cover.

Look at the title. What is it called when two or more words start with the same letter?[13]
Alliteration ✪

What adjective ✪ is used to describe Corey?[13]
Cranky

What is the meaning of the word 'cranky'?[14]
Cranky: bad-tempered, irritable, crabby

Have you ever been cranky?
Reader to give a personal response
If the answer is yes, ask:[1]
What do you feel when you are cranky?
We can feel annoyed, irritable and on edge. We don't tolerate things as well as usual and therefore we can get annoyed with simple things that happen.
If no, ask:
Have you ever been around someone who has been cranky?
Reader to give a personal response

What does it feel like to be around someone who is cranky?[1]
It can feel uncomfortable and awkward. It can also feel scary at times.

What can make you cranky?[1]
Reader to give a personal response

Monday

The lunchtime bell rang and Corey was the first person in his class to run out onto the playground. He hurriedly grabbed a basketball as the captains chose their team members. During the fast-paced game, Corey missed the basket and stormed off in a huff.

Page Two

Allow the reader to read the text aloud.

What is the main idea ⭐ in this text?[16]
Corey was cranky during the game of basketball because he missed a goal.

➡️ What is the setting ⭐ of the story?[5]
The story is in a school setting.

➡️ Which clues in the text help you to infer ⭐ the setting of the story?[8]
The text refers to the lunchtime bell ringing, and the playground.

➡️ How did Corey behave when things didn't go his way?[4]
He 'stormed off in a huff'.

➡️ Can you replace the word 'grabbed' with a synonym ⭐ ?[14]
Synonyms: grasped, snatched, plucked, gripped

Page Three

Allow the reader to study the illustration.

Look at the visual information the illustration is giving you. How does the illustrator show that Corey is very angry?[7]

Steam is coming out of his ears

His mouth is opened like he is screaming

His eyes are tightly closed

He is squeezing the basketball

Is Corey's behaviour appropriate in any sport or game? Why/why not?[2]

No, it is not appropriate. Everyone gets disappointed during a game, but they need to carry on because each person is an important part of the team.

What advice would you give Corey to change his behaviour?[1]

Calm yourself down

Continue in the game

Don't give up so easily

Tuesday

Corey was caught up in a game of handball. The ball came his way, but just as he was about to return the ball with a hit, he missed it. Everyone called, 'Out' in unison. Corey felt like his face was on fire as he stormed off.

Page Four

➡ What does it mean to be 'caught up' in a game?[14]

To become involved and focused on the game

Do you ever get caught up in something?

Reader to give a personal response

What does the word 'unison' mean? Can you try to work it out from the context (from within the sentence or part of the story in which the word is written)?[14]

Unison: the children all spoke together, simultaneously

➡ What possible reasons could make everyone call 'out' in unison?[8]

Everyone is involved in the game and is eager to be the next person in.

Everyone is excited about the competition.

If everyone calls 'out' for all the players, then it is not being mean; it is a part of the game.

From what you know about the character so far, do you think he stormed off because people called 'out'?[8]

No, it's more likely that he stormed off because he missed the ball.

➡ Is Corey's face literally ⭐ on fire?[8]

No, the word is used figuratively. His face only feels like it's on fire.

Wednesday

During afternoon sport time, Corey was batter up in a friendly game of cricket. When the ball was bowled to Corey, he hit it hard. It flew through the air, giving the batters time to get some much-needed runs. Spirits were high, but that all came to an end on Corey's fourth run when the ball came whistling through the air and hit the stumps.

'Out!' called the umpire.

Corey's happiness turned to frustration. He hunched his shoulders and looked down at the ground as he stomped off the pitch.

RW 100

RW 150

Page Six

➤ Allow the reader to read the text aloud.

Are there any words that you are unsure of?[14]
If the answer is no, ask:

What does 'batter up' mean? Can you try to work it out from the context (from within the sentence or part of the story in which the word is written)?
Batter up: the next person's turn to bat

➤ What is the meaning of 'whistling through the air'?[11]
The ball was like a projectile and made a whistling sound as it flew through the air.

As a good reader, how does this descriptive language ⭐ help you?[12]
It creates a specific image and sound that helps the reader visualise what is happening.

➤ How did Corey's body language show that he was not happy?[5]
His shoulders were hunched, his eyes were down, and he stomped off the field.

➤ What caused this reaction?[5]
He got out.

➤ Which words are *cricket words* (cricket terminology)?[14]

Batter up: it is the next person's turn to bat
Bowled: the cricket ball is being thrown to the batter
Batter: the person who is batting
Run: the batter hits the ball away from the fielders so they and their partner can run the length of the pitch
Stumps: three posts making up a wicket
Umpire: a person who enforces the rules of a game
Pitch: the rectangular surface in the centre of the field where most of the action takes place

Thursday

During recess, Corey asked his friends if he could join in on their game. They all looked at each other with hesitation, afraid to let him play.

Bradley walked over to Corey and said, 'Corey, if you play in our team, you can't storm off if you get out.'

Every time you get cranky when you get out,' Kirsten explained, 'it spoils everyone's fun and the team feels let down.'

Page Eight

Allow the reader to read the text aloud.

Why were the friends hesitating before speaking to Corey?[8]

They were afraid to let him play.

They were unsure of what to say to him.

They looked at each other, hoping that someone would say something to him.

Why do you think Corey's friends were afraid to let him play?[5]

- They didn't like how he acted when he got out.
- He threw tantrums and stormed off when he got out.
- He spoiled the game for the rest of the players.

Have you ever been in a situation like Corey's friends, where you've felt uncomfortable saying something?[1]

If the answer is yes, reader to give a personal response

If no, ask:

If you were one of Corey's friends, would you feel uncomfortable?

Reader to give a personal response

How did Corey's friends deal with it?[9]

Corey's friends were open and honest. They stated the problem and explained the effect his behaviour had on those around him.

Page Nine

Allow the reader to study the illustration.

How has the illustrator given you more information about how the friends are feeling?[7]

You can see the emotion on each of their faces. They looked worried and apprehensive.

'Everyone gets out at some time,' Mario added. 'It's important to be a good sport and continue with the game even if you feel disappointed. You're a team member, so you should cheer for someone else and enjoy the rest of the game without sulking or being angry.'

Page Ten

Allow the reader to read the text aloud.

 What advice did Mario give Corey?[4]
It's important to be a good sport.
It's okay to feel disappointed, but you need to cheer on someone else.
Don't sulk or be angry.
Enjoy the rest of the game.

What possible reactions do you think Corey could have to what Kirsten was saying?[3]
Upset, annoyed, angry, apologetic, accepting

How would you feel if you were Corey hearing this information?[1]
Reader to give a personal response

Corey was surprised by what his friends were telling him. He'd never really thought about the way his behaviour could affect other people. He only ever thought about how *he* was feeling. He was sorry for the way he had behaved.

'I'm sorry,' he said, 'but I get so disappointed when I don't win that I lose my cool. I'll think about what you've all said and try to be a better sport. I know I need to be responsible for my behaviour. I might need your help and patience when I get it wrong, but I will try to do better.'

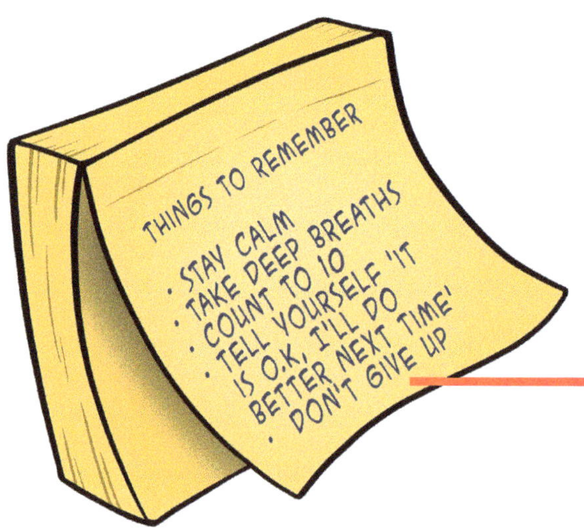

Page Eleven

Allow the reader to read the text aloud.

➤ Why was Corey surprised by what Kirsten said?[5]
It could have been the first time anyone had ever said anything to him about his behaviour.

➤ Why is the pronoun 'he' in italics?[13]
It emphasises that Corey thought only about his own feelings and not others.

Is it possible that he never considered how his behaviour affected other people?[18]
Yes. Sometimes we all get caught up in our own feelings, especially when we are angry.

Throughout the story, in which ways did Corey exhibit (show) that he was losing his cool?[5]
Encourage the reader to skim and scan ✪ the previous pages if they are unable to recall the behaviours.

- Stormed off in a huff
- Hunched his shoulders
- Looked down at the ground
- Stomped off

➤ Why did Corey have to be responsible for his own behaviour?[8]
When you take responsibility for your own failures/actions, you develop self-respect and this allows other people to respect you.

➤ What does Corey mean by 'help and patience'?[6]
His friends can help by giving him reminders, modelling good choices, and talking about how he is feeling.
His friends can show patience by not being annoyed if Corey takes a while to change his behaviour.

➤ There is a note on the page that is different to the text. What is the purpose of the note?[10]
The note helps by giving Corey ways to cope in situations that are challenging for him.

It took Corey some time to learn how to keep his cool whenever he got out of a game. His friends helped him by being positive, and reminding him to calm down and take deep breaths when he started to feel cranky. Corey began to enjoy playing games even when he didn't win, and his friends enjoyed having him play in their team.

Page Twelve

Allow the reader to read the text aloud.

What are the main ideas ⭐ in this narrative?[16]

Corey was someone who had difficulty controlling his disappointment when he got out of a game.

His friends were able to help him by being positive, reminding him to be calm and take deep breaths.

They were able to enjoy the game when Corey took responsibility and accepted getting out.

When a responsible person makes mistakes, they own it and work to make things right.

What is the main purpose of the narrative?[16]

It teaches a lesson about self-control and accepting responsibility.

What lesson did Corey learn?[6]

To calm himself down and to control his emotions
To be a good sport

Do you think it is possible for someone like Corey to change their behaviour?[19]

Corey is responsible for his own behaviour so it's possible for him to change it.

If you could rewrite the title, what would it be?[10]

Reader to give a response relevant to the storyline

If you could predict what might happen to Corey as a sequel to this story, what would it be?[19]

He became a good sport and helped younger students.

He was determined not to get out and practised at home.

He gave advice to younger children on how to control their anger.

Words and Phrases Used in Chronological Order

teachable moment   An unplanned opportunity that arises in the classroom where the teacher has an ideal chance to offer insight to their students; not something that can be planned for; a fleeting opportunity that must be sensed and seized by the teacher. If the reader is unable to answer the question, answers the question incorrectly, or after prompting is still unsure, take the opportunity to tell them the answer and show them how you reached that conclusion.

alliteration   Words that start with the same sound (not just the same letter) and are used repeatedly in a phrase or sentence (e.g. *Peter Piper picked a peck of pickled peppers*).

adjective   A word that describes a noun (e.g. a beautiful boy, a majestic swan).

main idea/s   Teaching readers to know what the main ideas are can be difficult. The main idea is the most important part of the story. It helps readers to understand what the story is mainly about without too much detail. Think of **who** and **what** to generate the main ideas.

infer   When you use clues from the story to figure out something that the author doesn't tell you. Using facts, observations and reasoning to come up with an assumption or conclusion (e.g. *The ground was wet and the leaves were moving around.* Inference: It had been raining and it was windy. *On Jocelyn's return from her holiday, her plants were limp and droopy.* Inference: Her plants had not been watered during the time that she was away.)

literally Taking a word or words in their usual sense without metaphor or exaggeration.

setting The setting within in a story is where and when an event takes place

synonym A word or phrase that means the same, or nearly the same, as another word or phrase in the same language.

descriptive language Language intended to create a mood, person, place, thing, event, emotion, or experience. Descriptive language uses images that appeal to the reader's senses, helping the reader to imagine how a subject looks, sounds, smells, tastes, or feels.

skim and scan To skim is to read text very quickly; to scan is to locate specific pieces of information in the text without having to read each individual word.

Learn with